# JACK AND JILL

Jack and Jill went up the hill,
To fetch a pail of water.
Jack fell down and broke his crown,
And Jill came tumbling after.

Up got Jack, and home did trot,
As fast as he could caper.
He went to bed and bound his head,
With vinegar and brown paper.

## OLD KING COLE

## PRETTY MAID

Pretty maid, pretty maid,
Where have you been?
Gathering a posie,
To give to the Queen.

Pretty maid, pretty maid,
What gave she you?
She gave me a diamond,
As big as my shoe.

Old King Cole,
Was a merry old soul,
And a merry old soul was he.

He called for his pipe,
And he called for his bowl,
And he called for his fiddlers three!

And every fiddler, he had a fine fiddl
And a very fine fiddle had he.
"Twee tweedle dee, tweedle dee,"
Went the fiddlers three.

Oh, there's none so rare,
As can compare,
With King Cole and his fiddlers thre

# THE QUEEN OF HEARTS

The Queen of Hearts,
She made some tarts,
All on a summer's day.

The Knave of Hearts,
He stole those tarts,
And took them clean away.

The King of Hearts,
Called for the tarts,
And beat the Knave full sore.

The Knave of Hearts,
Brought back the tarts,
And vowed he'd steal no more.

# I Saw Three Ships

I saw three ships come sailing by,
Come sailing by, come sailing by,
I saw three ships come sailing by,
On New Year's Day in the morning.

And what do you think was in them then
Was in them then, was in them then?
And what do you think was in them then
On New Year's Day in the morning?

Three pretty girls were in them then,
Were in them then, were in them then,
Three pretty girls were in them then,
On New Year's Day in the morning.

One could whistle, and one could sing,
And one could play the violin,
Such joy there was at my wedding,
On New Year's Day in the morning.

## Bobby Shaftoe

Bobby Shaftoe went to sea,
Silver buckles on his knee.
He'll come back and marry me,
Pretty Bobby Shaftoe.

Bobby Shaftoe's fine and fair,
Combing down his auburn hair.
He's my friend for ever more,
Pretty Bobby Shaftoe.

## Rub-A-Dub

Rub-a-dub-dub,
Three men in a tub,
And who do you think they be?
The butcher, the baker,
The candlestick maker.
They all sailed out to sea.

## INCY WINCY SPIDER

Incy wincy spider climbed up the water spout
Down came the rain and washed the spider ou
Out came the sun and dried up all the rain,
So incy wincy spider climbed up the spout agai

## LITTLE BO-PEEP

Little Bo-Peep has lost her sheep,
And can't tell where to find them.
Leave them alone, and they'll come home,
And bring their tails behind them.

# THE CROOKED SIXPENCE

There was a crooked man, and he went a crooked mile,
He found a crooked sixpence, beside a crooked stile,
He bought a crooked cat, which caught a crooked mouse,
And they all lived together, in a little crooked house.

# THE WHEELS ON THE BUS

The wheels on the bus go round and round,
Round and round, round and round.
The wheels on the bus go round and round,
All day long.
The horn on the bus goes toot toot toot,
Toot toot toot, toot toot toot.
The horn on the bus goes toot toot toot,
All day long.
The wipers on the bus go swish swish swish,
Swish swish swish, swish swish swish.
The wipers on the bus go swish swish swish,
All day long.
The people on the bus go up and down,
Up and down, up and down.
The people on the bus go up and down,
All day long.

## KING OF THE CASTLE

I'm the King of the castle,
Get down, you dirty rascal.
Get down, get down,
I'm the King of the castle.

## LONDON BRIDGE IS FALLING DOWN

London Bridge is falling down,
Falling down, falling down.
London Bridge is falling down,
My fair lady.

## LITTLE JACK HORNER

Little Jack Horner sat in the corner,
Eating a Christmas pie.
He put in his thumb,
And pulled out a plum,
And said, "What a good boy am I!"

## POLLY PUT THE KETTLE ON

Polly put the kettle on,
Polly put the kettle on,
Polly put the kettle on,
We'll all have tea.

Sukey take it off again,
Sukey take it off again,
Sukey take it off again,
They've all gone away.

## OLD MOTHER HUBBARD

Old Mother Hubbard,
Went to the cupboard,
To give her poor dog a bone.
But when she got there,
The cupboard was bare,
And so the poor dog had none.

## I'M A LITTLE TEAPOT

I'm a little teapot short and stout,
Here is my handle, here is my spout,
When I get all steamed up, hear me shout,
"Tip me over and pour me out."

# HICKORY DICKORY DOCK

Hickory dickory dock,
The mouse ran up the clock.
The clock struck one,
The mouse ran down,
Hickory dickory dock.

## Once I Saw A Little Bird

Once l saw a little bird,
Go hop, hop, hop.
So I cried, little bird,
Will you stop, stop, stop?
And I was going to the window,
To say, how do you do?
When he shook his little tail,
And away he flew.

# OLD MACDONALD

Old MacDonald had a farm, E-I-E-I-O.
And on that farm he had some ducks, E-I-E-I-O.
With a **quack quack** here and a **quack quack** there,
Here a **quack**, there a **quack**, everywhere a **quack, quack**
Old MacDonald had a farm, E-I-E-I-O.

Old MacDonald had a farm, E-I-E-I-O.
And on that farm he had some cows, E-I-E-I-O.
With a **moo moo** here and a **moo moo** there,
Here a **moo,** there a **moo,** everywhere a **moo, moo**.
Old MacDonald had a farm, E-I-E-I-O.

Old MacDonald had a farm, E-I-E-I-O.
And on that farm he had some sheep, E-I-E-I-O.
With a **baa baa** here and a **baa baa** there,
Here a **baa,** there a **baa,** everywhere a **baa, baa**
Old MacDonald had a farm, E-I-E-I-O.

Old MacDonald had a farm, E-I-E-I-O.
And on that farm he had some pigs, E-I-E-I-O.
With a **oink oink** here and a **oink oink** there,
Here a **oink,** there a **oink,** everywhere a **oink, oink**.
Old MacDonald had a farm, E-I-E-I-O.

## Baa, Baa, Black Sheep

Baa, baa, black sheep,
Have you any wool?
Yes, sir, yes, sir,
Three bags full.
One for my master,
And one for my dame,
And one for the little boy
Who lives down the lane.

## The Mulberry Bush

Here we go round the mulberry bush,
The mulberry bush, the mulberry bush.
Here we go round the mulberry bush,
So early in the morning.

## Mary, Mary

Mary, Mary quite contrary,
How does your garden grow?
With silver bells and cockle shells,
And pretty maids all in a row.

# Round And Round The Garden

Round and round the garden,
Like a teddy bear.
One step, two step,
Tickle you under there.

# Two Little Dicky Birds

Two little dicky birds,
Sat upon a wall.
One named Peter,
The other named Paul.
Fly away Peter,
Fly away Paul.
Come back Peter,
Come back Paul.

# Sing a Song of Sixpence

Sing a song of sixpence,
A pocket full of rye.
Four-and-twenty blackbirds,
Baked in a pie!

When the pie was opened,
The birds began to sing.
Was not that a dainty dish,
To set before the king?

The King was in his counting-house,
Counting out his money.
The Queen was in the parlor,
Eating bread and honey.

The maid was in the garden,
Hanging out the clothes.
When down came a blackbird,
And snapped off her nose.

## Humpty Dumpty

Humpty Dumpty sat on a wall.
Humpty Dumpty had a great fall.
All the King's horses and all the King's men,
Couldn't put Humpty together again.

## The Lion And The Unicorn

The lion and the unicorn,
Were fighting for the crown.
The lion beat the unicorn,
All about the town.

Some gave them white bread,
And some gave them brown.
Some gave them plum cake,
And sent them out of town.

## STAR LIGHT, STAR BRIGHT

Star light, star bright,
The first star I see tonight,
I wish I may, I wish I might,
Have the wish I wish tonight.

## TWINKLE, TWINKLE, LITTLE STAR

Twinkle, twinkle, little star,
How I wonder what you are.
Up above the world so high,
Like a diamond in the sky.
Twinkle, twinkle, little star,
How I wonder what you are.

## The Man In The Moon

The man in the moon came tumbling down,
And asked the way to Norwich.
He went by the south, and burnt his mouth,
With eating cold pease porridge.

## Early To Bed

Early to bed,
Early to rise.
Makes little Johnny,
Wealthy and wise.

# HEY DIDDLE DIDDLE

Hey diddle diddle,
The cat and the fiddle,
The cow jumped over the moon.

The little dog laughed,
To see such fun,
And the dish ran away,
With the spoon!